This Journal Belongs to:

____

Live Bold and Bloom

www.liveboldandbloom.com

3 THINGS A DAY:

A Minimalist Journal for More Focus with Less Stress

Created by Barrie Davenport

A Gift for You

As a way of saying thank you for purchasing this journal, please join the 3 Things A Day companion course. You'll have access to support materials that will help you stay on track with your daily goals as you work through this journal. You can join this free course here:

3thingsaday.com

About Barrie Davenport

Barrie Davenport is a certified personal coach, thought leader, author, and creator of several online courses on mindfulness, relationships, self-confidence, life passion, habit creation, and self-publishing. She is the founder of the top-ranked personal development site, Live Bold and Bloom.com. Her work as a coach, blogger, and author is focused on offering people practical strategies for living happier, more successful, and more mindful lives. She utilizes time-tested, evidence-based, action-oriented principles and methods to create real and measurable results for self-improvement.

You can learn more about Barrie on her Amazon author page at **barriedavenport.com/author**.

LESS

is

MORE

Ludwig Mies van der Rohe

The Myth of More

Imagine this: You sit down at your desk or kitchen table with paper and pen. You begin to write down everything you want to accomplish for the day. As your list grows longer, you heart starts racing and a low-level anxiety sets in.

How will you get it all done?

But you must because you've written it down. Every item feels necessary. You double-down on your resolve, but just as you're about to tackle the first item, the phone rings.

While you're on the phone, you open your computer and notice your inbox is full. You see several critical emails, so you decide to knock these out first. Before you know it, it's 11:00 am, and you haven't checked off the first item on your list. Now you feel deflated and overwhelmed.

"When you are pursuing any task with great anxiety, it takes a tremendous effort to realize a meager result," says Chin-Ning Chu, author of the book, *Do Less,*

Achieve More. "You are desiring and thinking so much; you are tired even before you start to work. Though your body has performed no task, your mind has been working hard at fighting and resisting your perceived circumstances."

Doing more to get more done is a myth — but it's a myth that Western culture has been promoting since the Industrial Revolution. Set more goals. Work more hours. Take fewer breaks.

Setting goals is useful but only as far as the goals are achievable. If you Google the phrase, "how to set goals," you'll find 762,000,000 results. There are millions of ways to set goals, but really only one way to achieve them — by consistently following through.

But the follow-through is the conumdrum, isn't it? We have the best intentions, the true desire to reach our goals and improve our lives, but taking action often eludes us.

In fact, research has proven that most of us who set goals at the start of a new year won't be successful at accomplishing what we resolve to do. You've probably experienced this yourself.

You have a big plan for exercising, learning a new skill, or finishing a project, but over the course of a few weeks or even days, you give up. It's not because you are lazy or incapable. For most of us, it's because we bite off more than we can chew.

When you try to accomplish too much on any given day or week, you set yourself up for failure. Establishing new habits and reaching big goals is difficult. It requires understanding and practicing a specific set of skills which involves retraining your brain.

Our brains are filled with neural pathways, formed by your oldest habits and memories. These pathways are strengthened every time you repeat a familiar action. With every goal or habit you add, your brain has to alter existing patterns in order to accommodate this new behavior.

That's why it's so important to apply a minimalist mindset when it comes to getting stuff done:

LESS IS MORE

When you give yourself less to accomplish, you make room in your psyche to achieve more. Why is that? Because you aren't flooding your brain with more new behaviors than it is capable of adopting at any given time.

Also, you're not overwhelming yourself with so many items on your list that you can't enjoy or savor what you're doing in the moment. When you slow down, focus more on the process than the outcome, and give yourself the space to be thoughtful, thorough, and in the flow, you'll have more mental energy to apply to other endeavors.

A Minimalist Mindset

Our culture reveres productivity. We've been trained to believe that the more we can get done in a specific timeframe, the more productive we are.

Time is money, and if you aren't producing optimally, you are costing yourself or your employer money. But studies suggest that we have this all wrong. The average employee is productive for only about three hours a day and can focus on a task for 20 minutes before losing steam.

In most work environments, employees spend too many hours "being busy" without being truly productive. We stay busy because we need to prove our value and feel guilty or anxious if we take time for recharging, thinking, or just taking a break.

John Trougakos, associate professor of Organizational Behavior and HR Management at the University of Toronto has found that we only have a certain amount of mental bandwidth for productivity.

"All efforts to control behavior, to perform and to focus

draw on that pool of psychological energy," he says in an article for *Fast Company*. "Once that energy source is depleted, we become less effective at everything that we do,"

Many studies have shown that working longer hours and cramming dozens of items on your project or to-do list *does not* make you more productive. Our brains are simply not meant to focus for a full eight hours a day.

Overwork and the resulting stress can lead to a variety of health issues, including sleep problems, depression, heavy drinking, diabetes, impaired memory, and heart disease.

However, working *with purpose* for short periods of time and taking frequent breaks does improve productivity and quality of work while reducing stress. Working with purpose means being in a state of "flow" in which you are deeply engaged with full concentration on the task at hand. You can't sustain this state for hours at a time.

This minimalist approach to getting more done involves several shifts in the typical attitudes about productivity.

You will need to:

- Shorten the number of hours you work in a day to preserve brain power and energy.
- Reduce the number of goals or tasks you pursue each day, focusing on the most critical tasks first.
- Limit the amount of time you spend focused on a task to 30 minutes to an hour.
- Remove all distractions and potential interruptions so you remain focused.
- Avoid multi-tasking completely.
- Take frequent breaks throughout the day, getting away from your work entirely.
- Savor what you are working on during the process of working.
- Acknowledge what you've accomplished with small rewards.

The best place to begin shifting to a minimalist but more productive work day is with your daily task list. For most of us, our daily lists contain anywhere from 10 to 20 items or more. You "brain dump" everything you can think of that needs action and then race like hell to get it all checked off by the end of the day.

However, changing this one habit can create a seismic shift in the quality of your work, your energy levels, and your attitude about the work you are doing. Rather than creating a daily list of a dozen things to accomplish in a day, limit your list to just three things a day. Yep, just three.

The Power of Three

You might wonder,"Why just three things a day? Why not five or seven?"

The answer is: Because setting three daily goals is measurable, manageable, and realistic.

In our hectic and distracted lives, where we are pummeled with information and distractions, limiting our daily goals to just three feels like a breath of fresh air. It takes the pressure off to "get it all done" when it's not in our best interest to attempt more than we can accomplish thoroughly, mindfully, and with any sense of joy.

You may ultimately accomplish five or fifteen tasks in your day, but at least you know every day that you have completed the three most important with focus and clarity. If you only complete those three action items, you have the satisfaction of knowing you completed them well.

Remember, most of us are genuinely productive for about three hours a day, maybe four. We can't maintain the mental energy required for intense and concentrated work for more than a few hours.

When you limit your most important daily action items to three, you optimize those productive hours by allowing the time and brain power to accomplish them thoroughly — without the pressure of knowing you have a list of other tasks you *must* accomplish.

Also, we tend to be more focused and alert in the morning hours before lunch. Then we begin to fade in the afternoon. The morning hours are the time to get your most important tasks completed while your energy is high.

Defining the three most important tasks (of about an hour each) for your day allows you to take advantage of the morning hours before the afternoon slump. You get these out of the way before your motivation wanes.

Let's say you begin work (or home tasks) at 8:30 am. You can work on your first task from 8:45 to 9:45, followed by a 15-minute break. Then you work on your second task from 10:00 am until 11:00 am and take a break until 11:15. You'll work on your last task from 11:15 until 12:15 pm, followed by your lunch break. This leaves plenty of time in the afternoon to tie up loose ends on these items or work on other less mentally-taxing tasks.

When you can say to yourself, "I completed my most important tasks before lunch," it's a huge boost to your sense of accomplishment. Everything else feels like gravy. You have more energy to tackle other less critical action items later in the day.

With just three things a day, you...

- Have more time to devote to each task.
- Have more mental stamina to complete each task.
- Feel less overwhelmed and agitated by your to-do list.
- Enjoy more engagement and focus with each action item.
- Will be more thorough, creative, and competent with the action items.
- Feel more satisfaction by completing your three most challenging tasks first.
- Can more easily develop the habit of completing your daily action items.
- Can accomplish more in a year because you're more likely to follow through.

How to Use This Journal

The beauty of this journal is its simplicity. Write down your three things each day, do them, and then check them off. Your goal with the journal is to never break the chain of checked-off boxes.

Just seeing all of those boxes lined up with checkmarks will give you a feeling of pride and accomplishment — the way you felt as a kid when you saw gold stars on your school assignments.

In order to "never break the chain" of checked boxes, you'll need to think carefully about the three action items you write down each day to ensure that you can complete them. These action items can be daily personal tasks, action steps that are part of a bigger project or long-term goal, or your most critical work tasks for the day.

Be sure that you . . .

☐ View the three action items as the most important for the day and non-negotiable.

☐ Write down the tasks the night before or early in the morning each day.

☐ Plan to complete the items in the morning before lunch if possible.

☐ Begin with the most difficult or creative task first.

☐ Are able to complete each item thoroughly, thoughtfully, and with full focus in an hour or less for each one.

☐ Break down larger tasks or projects into smaller ones you can complete in an hour or less if necessary.

☐ Group several small errands into one "errand" task that takes an hour or less.

- ☐ Have any tools, supplies, or resources ready in advance of working on the action item.
- ☐ Remove all distractions, turn off your phone, shut down other computer browsers, and deal with possible interruptions before you begin.
- ☐ Set a timer if necessary so you know when to finish up your action item.
- ☐ Take a 15 to 20-minute break between tasks where you do something relaxing.
- ☐ Acknowledge completing each action by checking it off in this journal.
- ☐ Celebrate completing a week's worth of action items by rewarding yourself. Write down your reward in the space provided at the end of each week.
- ☐ Never break the chain of checked boxes.

Your Weekly Reward

Celebrating your weekly achievements with this journal is a big part of maintaining your motivation. Each day you will acknowledge a job well-done by checking off your three action items. That's a small celebration in itself.

But at the end of the week, do something special for yourself — something you look forward to as a reward for completing your daily tasks for seven days straight. It shouldn't be something you plan to do anyway, like going out to dinner or watching a movie.

Plan a reward that you will receive only if you check off all 21 items for the week. Maybe you buy yourself something special, go for a massage, or allow yourself to binge-watch your favorite TV series.

Create Accountability

To help ensure your success with this journal, set up a system of accountability for completing your three things a day. There are many ways to do this:

- Find an online forum, support group, or blog where you can report your goals and progress.

- Use social media like Facebook and Twitter for accountability.

- Ask your spouse, friend, or a close family member to help you stay accountable.

- Use an accountability app like Asana.com or Goals Wizard.com.

If You Break the Chain

You might forget to set your three daily tasks. You might have an emergency or some unexpected situation arise that makes it impossible to achieve your goals. You might miscalculate how much time one or more of your items takes to complete, so you can't complete all three in one day.

If this happens (and it likely will), please don't use it as an excuse to stop working on this journal altogether. Yes, the chain will be broken, but you can go back and fix it by completing the tasks as soon as you are able — either the same day or another day.

Another option is to assign yourself three easy and short tasks that you can accomplish within an hour, and make these three short tasks the fourth task for the following day.

For example, on Monday you forget to write down and complete your three things. So on Tuesday morning, after you complete your three primary action items for the day, you might decide to straighten your desk, answer a couple of emails, and call a client. You can write these in for Monday's tasks, complete them quickly, and check them off — keeping the chain intact.

Do your best, and don't shame yourself if you mess up. Just keep trying to complete the items for all of the weeks. By the end of 52 weeks, you will have completed 1092 action items. That's a huge accomplishment!

DAY 3

Date

Thing 1 ☐

Thing 2 ☐

Thing 3 ☐

DAY 4

Date

Thing 1 ☐

Thing 2 ☐

Thing 3 ☐

DAY 5

Date

Thing 1 ☐

Thing 2 ☐

Thing 3 ☐

DAY 6

Date

Thing 1 ☐

Thing 2 ☐

Thing 3 ☐

DAY 7

Date

Thing 1 ☐

Thing 2 ☐

Thing 3 ☐

Week 2 – REWARD

Energy is the essence of life. Every day you decide how you're going to use it by knowing what you want and what it takes to reach that goal, and by maintaining focus.

— Oprah Winfrey

WEEK 3

DAY 1

Date

Thing 1 ☐

Thing 2 ☐

Thing 3 ☐

DAY 2

Date

Thing 1 ☐

Thing 2 ☐

Thing 3 ☐

DAY 3

Date

Thing 1

Thing 2

Thing 3

DAY 4

Date

Thing 1

Thing 2

Thing 3

DAY 5

Date

Thing 1 ☐

Thing 2 ☐

Thing 3 ☐

DAY 6

Date

Thing 1 ☐

Thing 2 ☐

Thing 3 ☐

DAY 7

Date

Thing 1 ☐

Thing 2 ☐

Thing 3 ☐

Week 3 – REWARD

Multi-tasking is merely the opportunity to screw up more than one thing at a time.

— Gary W. Keller

WEEK 4

DAY 1

Date

Thing 1 ☐

Thing 2 ☐

Thing 3 ☐

DAY 2

Date

Thing 1 ☐

Thing 2 ☐

Thing 3 ☐

DAY 3

Date

Thing 1 ☐

Thing 2 ☐

Thing 3 ☐

DAY 4

Date

Thing 1 ☐

Thing 2 ☐

Thing 3 ☐

DAY 5

Date

Thing 1 ☐

Thing 2 ☐

Thing 3 ☐

DAY 6

Date

Thing 1 ☐

Thing 2 ☐

Thing 3 ☐

DAY 7

Date

Thing 1 ______________________ ☐

____

Thing 2 ______________________ ☐

____

Thing 3 ______________________ ☐

____

Week 4 – REWARD

____

____

____

____

To be everywhere is to be nowhere.

— Seneca

WEEK 5

DAY 1

Date

Thing 1

Thing 2

Thing 3

DAY 2

Date

Thing 1

Thing 2

Thing 3

DAY 3

Date

Thing 1 ☐

Thing 2 ☐

Thing 3 ☐

DAY 4

Date

Thing 1 ☐

Thing 2 ☐

Thing 3 ☐

DAY 5

Date

Thing 1

Thing 2

Thing 3

DAY 6

Date

Thing 1

Thing 2

Thing 3

DAY 7

Date

Thing 1 ☐

Thing 2 ☐

Thing 3 ☐

Week 5 – REWARD

May what I do flow from me like a river, no forcing and no holding back, the way it is with children.

— Rainer Maria Rilke

WEEK 6

DAY 1

Date

Thing 1 ☐

Thing 2 ☐

Thing 3 ☐

DAY 2

Date

Thing 1 ☐

Thing 2 ☐

Thing 3 ☐

DAY 3

Date

Thing 1

Thing 2

Thing 3

DAY 4

Date

Thing 1

Thing 2

Thing 3

DAY 5

Date

Thing 1 ☐

Thing 2 ☐

Thing 3 ☐

DAY 6

Date

Thing 1 ☐

Thing 2 ☐

Thing 3 ☐

DAY 7

Date

Thing 1 ☐

Thing 2 ☐

Thing 3 ☐

Week 6 – REWARD

May your work be in keeping with your purpose.

— Leonardo da Vinci

WEEK 7

DAY 1

Date

Thing 1 ☐

Thing 2 ☐

Thing 3 ☐

DAY 2

Date

Thing 1 ☐

Thing 2 ☐

Thing 3 ☐

DAY 3

Date

Thing 1 ☐

Thing 2 ☐

Thing 3 ☐

DAY 4

Date

Thing 1 ☐

Thing 2 ☐

Thing 3 ☐

DAY 5

Date

Thing 1

Thing 2

Thing 3

DAY 6

Date

Thing 1

Thing 2

Thing 3

DAY 7

Date

Thing 1 ______________ ☐

Thing 2 ______________ ☐

Thing 3 ______________ ☐

Week 7 – REWARD

Working smart means wringing maximum production from your work schedule. It's coming up with new ideas to bring that about.

— Robert Terson

WEEK 8

DAY 1

Date

Thing 1 ☐

Thing 2 ☐

Thing 3 ☐

DAY 2

Date

Thing 1 ☐

Thing 2 ☐

Thing 3 ☐

DAY 3

Date

Thing 1 ☐

Thing 2 ☐

Thing 3 ☐

DAY 4

Date

Thing 1 ☐

Thing 2 ☐

Thing 3 ☐

DAY 5

Date

Thing 1

Thing 2

Thing 3

DAY 6

Date

Thing 1

Thing 2

Thing 3

DAY 7

Date

Thing 1 ☐

Thing 2 ☐

Thing 3 ☐

Week 8 – REWARD

Striving for excellence motivates you; striving for perfection is demoralizing.

— Harriet Braiker

WEEK 9

DAY 1

Date

Thing 1 ☐

Thing 2 ☐

Thing 3 ☐

DAY 2

Date

Thing 1 ☐

Thing 2 ☐

Thing 3 ☐

DAY 3

Date

Thing 1 ☐

Thing 2 ☐

Thing 3 ☐

DAY 4

Date

Thing 1 ☐

Thing 2 ☐

Thing 3 ☐

DAY 5

Date

Thing 1 ______ ☐

Thing 2 ______ ☐

Thing 3 ______ ☐

DAY 6

Date

Thing 1 ______ ☐

Thing 2 ______ ☐

Thing 3 ______ ☐

DAY 7

Date

Thing 1

Thing 2

Thing 3

Week 9 – REWARD

We think, mistakenly, that success is the result of the amount of time we put in at work, instead of the quality of time we put in.

— Arianna Huffington

WEEK 10

DAY 1

Date

Thing 1 ☐

Thing 2 ☐

Thing 3 ☐

DAY 2

Date

Thing 1 ☐

Thing 2 ☐

Thing 3 ☐

DAY 3

Date

Thing 1

Thing 2

Thing 3

DAY 4

Date

Thing 1

Thing 2

Thing 3

DAY 5

Date

Thing 1

Thing 2

Thing 3

DAY 6

Date

Thing 1

Thing 2

Thing 3

DAY 7

Date

Thing 1

Thing 2

Thing 3

Week 10 – REWARD

It is not enough to be busy; so are the ants. The question is: What are we busy about?

— Henry David Thoreau

WEEK 11

DAY 1

Date

Thing 1 ☐

Thing 2 ☐

Thing 3 ☐

DAY 2

Date

Thing 1 ☐

Thing 2 ☐

Thing 3 ☐

DAY 3

Date

Thing 1 ☐

Thing 2 ☐

Thing 3 ☐

DAY 4

Date

Thing 1 ☐

Thing 2 ☐

Thing 3 ☐

DAY 5

Date

Thing 1

Thing 2

Thing 3

DAY 6

Date

Thing 1

Thing 2

Thing 3

DAY 7

Date

Thing 1

Thing 2

Thing 3

Week 11 – REWARD

When you expect the world to end at any moment, you know there is no need to hurry. You take your time, you do your work well.

— Thomas Merton

WEEK 12

DAY 1

Date

Thing 1 ☐

Thing 2 ☐

Thing 3 ☐

DAY 2

Date

Thing 1 ☐

Thing 2 ☐

Thing 3 ☐

DAY 3

Date

Thing 1 ☐

Thing 2 ☐

Thing 3 ☐

DAY 4

Date

Thing 1 ☐

Thing 2 ☐

Thing 3 ☐

DAY 5

Date

Thing 1 ☐

Thing 2 ☐

Thing 3 ☐

DAY 6

Date

Thing 1 ☐

Thing 2 ☐

Thing 3 ☐

DAY 7

Date

Thing 1 ______________________ ☐

____

Thing 2 ______________________ ☐

____

Thing 3 ______________________ ☐

____

Week 12 - REWARD

____

____

____

____

Smart workers don't focus on inputs they focus on prioritizing in order to achieve the most valuable outputs in the most efficient ways.

— Jacob Morgan

WEEK 13

DAY 1

Date

Thing 1 ☐

Thing 2 ☐

Thing 3 ☐

DAY 2

Date

Thing 1 ☐

Thing 2 ☐

Thing 3 ☐

DAY 3

Date

Thing 1

Thing 2

Thing 3

DAY 4

Date

Thing 1

Thing 2

Thing 3

DAY 5

Date

Thing 1 ☐

Thing 2 ☐

Thing 3 ☐

DAY 6

Date

Thing 1 ☐

Thing 2 ☐

Thing 3 ☐

DAY 7

Date

Thing 1 ______________ ☐

Thing 2 ______________ ☐

Thing 3 ______________ ☐

Week 13 – REWARD

Trying to do it all and expecting that it all can be done exactly right is a recipe for disappointment. Perfection is the enemy.

— Sheryl Sandberg

WEEK 14

DAY 1

Date

Thing 1 ☐

Thing 2 ☐

Thing 3 ☐

DAY 2

Date

Thing 1 ☐

Thing 2 ☐

Thing 3 ☐

DAY 3

Date

Thing 1

Thing 2

Thing 3

DAY 4

Date

Thing 1

Thing 2

Thing 3

DAY 5

Date

Thing 1 ☐

Thing 2 ☐

Thing 3 ☐

DAY 6

Date

Thing 1 ☐

Thing 2 ☐

Thing 3 ☐

DAY 7

Date

Thing 1 ______

Thing 2 ______

Thing 3 ______

Week 14 – REWARD

When walking, walk. When eating, eat.

— Zen Proverb

WEEK 15

DAY 1

Date

Thing 1 ☐

Thing 2 ☐

Thing 3 ☐

DAY 2

Date

Thing 1 ☐

Thing 2 ☐

Thing 3 ☐

DAY 3

Date

Thing 1 ☐

Thing 2 ☐

Thing 3 ☐

DAY 4

Date

Thing 1 ☐

Thing 2 ☐

Thing 3 ☐

DAY 5

Date

Thing 1

Thing 2

Thing 3

DAY 6

Date

Thing 1

Thing 2

Thing 3

DAY 7

Date

Thing 1 ☐

Thing 2 ☐

Thing 3 ☐

Week 15 – REWARD

If you want to be happy, set a goal that commands your thoughts, liberates your energy and inspires your hopes.

— Andrew Carnegie

WEEK 16

DAY 1

Date

Thing 1 ☐

Thing 2 ☐

Thing 3 ☐

DAY 2

Date

Thing 1 ☐

Thing 2 ☐

Thing 3 ☐

DAY 3

Date

Thing 1

Thing 2

Thing 3

DAY 4

Date

Thing 1

Thing 2

Thing 3

DAY 5

Date

Thing 1 ☐

Thing 2 ☐

Thing 3 ☐

DAY 6

Date

Thing 1 ☐

Thing 2 ☐

Thing 3 ☐

DAY 7

Date

Thing 1 ☐

Thing 2 ☐

Thing 3 ☐

Week 16 – REWARD

Checking items off a to-do list doesn't determine progress; focusing on your priorities is what counts.

— Frank Sonnenberg

WEEK 17

DAY 1

Date

Thing 1 ☐

Thing 2 ☐

Thing 3 ☐

DAY 2

Date

Thing 1 ☐

Thing 2 ☐

Thing 3 ☐

DAY 3

Date

Thing 1 ☐

Thing 2 ☐

Thing 3 ☐

DAY 4

Date

Thing 1 ☐

Thing 2 ☐

Thing 3 ☐

DAY 5

Date

Thing 1 ☐

Thing 2 ☐

Thing 3 ☐

DAY 6

Date

Thing 1 ☐

Thing 2 ☐

Thing 3 ☐

DAY 7

Date

Thing 1 ☐

Thing 2 ☐

Thing 3 ☐

Week 17 – REWARD

Either you run the day, or the day runs you.

— Jim Rohn

WEEK 18

DAY 1

Date

Thing 1

Thing 2

Thing 3

DAY 2

Date

Thing 1

Thing 2

Thing 3

DAY 3

Date

Thing 1

Thing 2

Thing 3

DAY 4

Date

Thing 1

Thing 2

Thing 3

DAY 5

Date

Thing 1

Thing 2

Thing 3

DAY 6

Date

Thing 1

Thing 2

Thing 3

DAY 7

Date

Thing 1 ☐

Thing 2 ☐

Thing 3 ☐

Week 18 – REWARD

Balance is not better time management, but better boundary management. Balance means making choices and enjoying those choices.

— Betsy Jacobson

WEEK 19

DAY 1

Date

Thing 1 ☐

Thing 2 ☐

Thing 3 ☐

DAY 2

Date

Thing 1 ☐

Thing 2 ☐

Thing 3 ☐

DAY 3

Date

Thing 1 ☐

Thing 2 ☐

Thing 3 ☐

DAY 4

Date

Thing 1 ☐

Thing 2 ☐

Thing 3 ☐

DAY 5

Date

Thing 1 ☐

Thing 2 ☐

Thing 3 ☐

DAY 6

Date

Thing 1 ☐

Thing 2 ☐

Thing 3 ☐

DAY 7

Date

Thing 1 ☐

Thing 2 ☐

Thing 3 ☐

Week 19 – REWARD

One reason so few of us achieve what we truly want is that we never direct our focus; we never concentrate our power.

— Tony Robbins

WEEK 20

DAY 1

Date

Thing 1 ☐

Thing 2 ☐

Thing 3 ☐

DAY 2

Date

Thing 1 ☐

Thing 2 ☐

Thing 3 ☐

DAY 3

Date

Thing 1

Thing 2

Thing 3

DAY 4

Date

Thing 1

Thing 2

Thing 3

DAY 5

Date

Thing 1

Thing 2

Thing 3

DAY 6

Date

Thing 1

Thing 2

Thing 3

DAY 7

Date

Thing 1 ☐

Thing 2 ☐

Thing 3 ☐

Week 20 – REWARD

Concentrate all your thoughts upon the work at hand. The sun's rays do not burn until brought to a focus.

— Alexander Graham Bell

WEEK 21

DAY 1

Date

Thing 1 ☐

Thing 2 ☐

Thing 3 ☐

DAY 2

Date

Thing 1 ☐

Thing 2 ☐

Thing 3 ☐

DAY 3

Date

Thing 1

Thing 2

Thing 3

DAY 4

Date

Thing 1

Thing 2

Thing 3

DAY 5

Date

Thing 1

Thing 2

Thing 3

DAY 6

Date

Thing 1

Thing 2

Thing 3

DAY 7

Date

Thing 1 ☐

Thing 2 ☐

Thing 3 ☐

Week 21 – REWARD

The key to success is to focus our conscious mind on things we desire not things we fear.

— Brian Tracy

WEEK 22

DAY 1

Date

Thing 1 ☐

Thing 2 ☐

Thing 3 ☐

DAY 2

Date

Thing 1 ☐

Thing 2 ☐

Thing 3 ☐

DAY 3

Date

Thing 1 ☐

Thing 2 ☐

Thing 3 ☐

DAY 4

Date

Thing 1 ☐

Thing 2 ☐

Thing 3 ☐

DAY 5

Date

Thing 1 ☐

Thing 2 ☐

Thing 3 ☐

DAY 6

Date

Thing 1 ☐

Thing 2 ☐

Thing 3 ☐

DAY 7

Date

Thing 1

Thing 2

Thing 3

Week 22 – REWARD

One look at an email can rob you of 15 minutes of focus. One call on your cell phone, one tweet, one instant message can destroy your schedule . . . .

— Jacqueline Leo

WEEK 23

DAY 1

Date

Thing 1

Thing 2

Thing 3

DAY 2

Date

Thing 1

Thing 2

Thing 3

DAY 3

Date

Thing 1

Thing 2

Thing 3

DAY 4

Date

Thing 1

Thing 2

Thing 3

DAY 5

Date

Thing 1 ☐

Thing 2 ☐

Thing 3 ☐

DAY 6

Date

Thing 1 ☐

Thing 2 ☐

Thing 3 ☐

DAY 7

Date

Thing 1 ☐

Thing 2 ☐

Thing 3 ☐

Week 23 - REWARD

Being selective—doing less—is the path of the productive. Focus on the important few and ignore the rest.

— Tim Ferriss

WEEK 24

DAY 1

Date

Thing 1 ☐

Thing 2 ☐

Thing 3 ☐

DAY 2

Date

Thing 1 ☐

Thing 2 ☐

Thing 3 ☐

DAY 3

Date

Thing 1

Thing 2

Thing 3

DAY 4

Date

Thing 1

Thing 2

Thing 3

DAY 5

Date

Thing 1

Thing 2

Thing 3

DAY 6

Date

Thing 1

Thing 2

Thing 3

DAY 7

Date

Thing 1 ________ ☐

Thing 2 ________ ☐

Thing 3 ________ ☐

Week 24 – REWARD

My success, part of it certainly, is that I have focused in on a few things.

— Bill Gates

WEEK 25

DAY 1

Date

Thing 1

Thing 2

Thing 3

DAY 2

Date

Thing 1

Thing 2

Thing 3

DAY 3

Date

Thing 1 ☐

Thing 2 ☐

Thing 3 ☐

DAY 4

Date

Thing 1 ☐

Thing 2 ☐

Thing 3 ☐

DAY 5

Date

Thing 1 ☐

Thing 2 ☐

Thing 3 ☐

DAY 6

Date

Thing 1 ☐

Thing 2 ☐

Thing 3 ☐

DAY 7

Date

Thing 1

Thing 2

Thing 3

Week 25 – REWARD

Focus on the journey, not the destination. Joy is found not in finishing an activity but in doing it.

— Greg Anderson

WEEK 26

DAY 1

Date

Thing 1 ☐

Thing 2 ☐

Thing 3 ☐

DAY 2

Date

Thing 1 ☐

Thing 2 ☐

Thing 3 ☐

DAY 3

Date

Thing 1

Thing 2

Thing 3

DAY 4

Date

Thing 1

Thing 2

Thing 3

DAY 5

Date

Thing 1

Thing 2

Thing 3

DAY 6

Date

Thing 1

Thing 2

Thing 3

DAY 7

Date

Thing 1

Thing 2

Thing 3

Week 26 – REWARD

It's important to focus on what we do best and master one craft at a time.

— Russell Simmons

WEEK 27

DAY 1

Date

Thing 1 ☐

Thing 2 ☐

Thing 3 ☐

DAY 2

Date

Thing 1 ☐

Thing 2 ☐

Thing 3 ☐

DAY 3

Date

Thing 1 ☐

Thing 2 ☐

Thing 3 ☐

DAY 4

Date

Thing 1 ☐

Thing 2 ☐

Thing 3 ☐

DAY 5

Date

Thing 1 ☐

Thing 2 ☐

Thing 3 ☐

DAY 6

Date

Thing 1 ☐

Thing 2 ☐

Thing 3 ☐

DAY 7

Date

Thing 1

Thing 2

Thing 3

Week 27 – REWARD

Live in the moment, where everything is just right, take your time and limit your bad memories and you'll get wherever it is you're going a lot faster and with less bumps in the way.

— J.A. Redmerski

WEEK 28

DAY 1

Date

Thing 1 ☐

Thing 2 ☐

Thing 3 ☐

DAY 2

Date

Thing 1 ☐

Thing 2 ☐

Thing 3 ☐

DAY 3

Date

Thing 1 ☐

Thing 2 ☐

Thing 3 ☐

DAY 4

Date

Thing 1 ☐

Thing 2 ☐

Thing 3 ☐

DAY 5

Date

Thing 1 ☐

Thing 2 ☐

Thing 3 ☐

DAY 6

Date

Thing 1 ☐

Thing 2 ☐

Thing 3 ☐

DAY 7

Date

Thing 1

Thing 2

Thing 3

Week 28 – REWARD

The successful warrior is the average man, with laser-like focus.

— Bruce Lee

WEEK 29

DAY 1

Date

Thing 1 ☐

Thing 2 ☐

Thing 3 ☐

DAY 2

Date

Thing 1 ☐

Thing 2 ☐

Thing 3 ☐

DAY 3

Date

Thing 1

Thing 2

Thing 3

DAY 4

Date

Thing 1

Thing 2

Thing 3

DAY 5

Date

Thing 1 ☐

Thing 2 ☐

Thing 3 ☐

DAY 6

Date

Thing 1 ☐

Thing 2 ☐

Thing 3 ☐

DAY 7

Date

Thing 1 ________ ☐

Thing 2 ________ ☐

Thing 3 ________ ☐

Week 29 – REWARD

What looks like multitasking is really switching back and forth between multiple tasks, which reduces productivity and increases mistakes by up to 50 percent.

— Susan Cain

WEEK 30

DAY 1

Date

Thing 1 ☐

Thing 2 ☐

Thing 3 ☐

DAY 2

Date

Thing 1 ☐

Thing 2 ☐

Thing 3 ☐

DAY 3

Date

Thing 1

Thing 2

Thing 3

DAY 4

Date

Thing 1

Thing 2

Thing 3

DAY 5

Date

Thing 1 ☐

Thing 2 ☐

Thing 3 ☐

DAY 6

Date

Thing 1 ☐

Thing 2 ☐

Thing 3 ☐

DAY 7

Date

Thing 1

Thing 2

Thing 3

Week 30 – REWARD

Most people have no idea of the giant capacity we can immediately command when we focus all of our resources on mastering a single area of our lives.

— Tony Robbins

WEEK 31

DAY 1

Date

Thing 1 ☐

Thing 2 ☐

Thing 3 ☐

DAY 2

Date

Thing 1 ☐

Thing 2 ☐

Thing 3 ☐

DAY 3

Date

Thing 1

Thing 2

Thing 3

DAY 4

Date

Thing 1

Thing 2

Thing 3

DAY 5

Date

Thing 1 ☐

Thing 2 ☐

Thing 3 ☐

DAY 6

Date

Thing 1 ☐

Thing 2 ☐

Thing 3 ☐

DAY 7

Date

Thing 1

Thing 2

Thing 3

Week 31 – REWARD

Working hard for something we don't care about is called stress: Working hard for something we love is called passion.

— Simon Sinek

WEEK 32

DAY 1

Date

Thing 1 ☐

Thing 2 ☐

Thing 3 ☐

DAY 2

Date

Thing 1 ☐

Thing 2 ☐

Thing 3 ☐

DAY 3

Date

Thing 1

Thing 2

Thing 3

DAY 4

Date

Thing 1

Thing 2

Thing 3

DAY 5

Date

Thing 1

Thing 2

Thing 3

DAY 6

Date

Thing 1

Thing 2

Thing 3

DAY 7

Date

Thing 1 ☐

Thing 2 ☐

Thing 3 ☐

Week 32 – REWARD

Burnout is about resentment. Preventing it is about knowing yourself well enough to know what it is you're giving up that makes you resentful.

— Marissa Mayer

WEEK 33

DAY 1

Date

Thing 1 ☐

Thing 2 ☐

Thing 3 ☐

DAY 2

Date

Thing 1 ☐

Thing 2 ☐

Thing 3 ☐

DAY 3

Date

Thing 1 ☐

Thing 2 ☐

Thing 3 ☐

DAY 4

Date

Thing 1 ☐

Thing 2 ☐

Thing 3 ☐

DAY 5

Date

Thing 1

Thing 2

Thing 3

DAY 6

Date

Thing 1

Thing 2

Thing 3

DAY 7

Date

Thing 1

Thing 2

Thing 3

Week 33 – REWARD

Many people feel they must multi-task because everybody else is multitasking, but this is partly because they are all interrupting each other so much.

— Marilyn vos Savant

WEEK 34

DAY 1

Date

Thing 1 ☐

Thing 2 ☐

Thing 3 ☐

DAY 2

Date

Thing 1 ☐

Thing 2 ☐

Thing 3 ☐

DAY 3

Date

Thing 1

Thing 2

Thing 3

DAY 4

Date

Thing 1

Thing 2

Thing 3

DAY 5

Date

Thing 1

Thing 2

Thing 3

DAY 6

Date

Thing 1

Thing 2

Thing 3

DAY 7

Date

Thing 1

Thing 2

Thing 3

Week 34 – REWARD

I used to work extremely hard and didn't really achieve a lot of tangible things. But when I started working extremely smart,the gates of abundant blessings opened up for me.

— Edmond Mbiaka

WEEK 35

DAY 1

Date

Thing 1 ☐

Thing 2 ☐

Thing 3 ☐

DAY 2

Date

Thing 1 ☐

Thing 2 ☐

Thing 3 ☐

DAY 3

Date

Thing 1

Thing 2

Thing 3

DAY 4

Date

Thing 1

Thing 2

Thing 3

DAY 5

Date

Thing 1 ☐

Thing 2 ☐

Thing 3 ☐

DAY 6

Date

Thing 1 ☐

Thing 2 ☐

Thing 3 ☐

DAY 7

Date

Thing 1

Thing 2

Thing 3

Week 35 – REWARD

People who work hard and people who work smart have different measures of success.

— Jacob Morgan

WEEK 36

DAY 1

Date

Thing 1 ☐

Thing 2 ☐

Thing 3 ☐

DAY 2

Date

Thing 1 ☐

Thing 2 ☐

Thing 3 ☐

DAY 3

Date

Thing 1

Thing 2

Thing 3

DAY 4

Date

Thing 1

Thing 2

Thing 3

DAY 5

Date

Thing 1 ☐

Thing 2 ☐

Thing 3 ☐

DAY 6

Date

Thing 1 ☐

Thing 2 ☐

Thing 3 ☐

DAY 7

Date

Thing 1 ☐

Thing 2 ☐

Thing 3 ☐

Week 36 – REWARD

I do what I do, and I do it well, and focus and take it one moment at a time.

— James Caviezel

WEEK 37

DAY 1

Date

Thing 1 ☐

Thing 2 ☐

Thing 3 ☐

DAY 2

Date

Thing 1 ☐

Thing 2 ☐

Thing 3 ☐

DAY 3

Date

Thing 1 ☐

Thing 2 ☐

Thing 3 ☐

DAY 4

Date

Thing 1 ☐

Thing 2 ☐

Thing 3 ☐

DAY 5

Date

Thing 1 ☐

Thing 2 ☐

Thing 3 ☐

DAY 6

Date

Thing 1 ☐

Thing 2 ☐

Thing 3 ☐

DAY 7

Date

Thing 1

Thing 2

Thing 3

Week 37 – REWARD

Lack of direction, not lack of time, is the problem.
We all have twenty-four hour days.

— Zig Ziglar

WEEK 38

DAY 1

Date

Thing 1

Thing 2

Thing 3

DAY 2

Date

Thing 1

Thing 2

Thing 3

DAY 3

Date

Thing 1 ☐

Thing 2 ☐

Thing 3 ☐

DAY 4

Date

Thing 1 ☐

Thing 2 ☐

Thing 3 ☐

DAY 5

Date

Thing 1 ________

Thing 2 ________

Thing 3 ________

DAY 6

Date

Thing 1 ________

Thing 2 ________

Thing 3 ________

DAY 7

Date

Thing 1 ______________ ☐

Thing 2 ______________ ☐

Thing 3 ______________ ☐

Week 38 – REWARD

The elevator to success is out of order. You'll have to use the stairs... one step at a time.

— Joe Girard

WEEK 39

DAY 1

Date

Thing 1 ☐

Thing 2 ☐

Thing 3 ☐

DAY 2

Date

Thing 1 ☐

Thing 2 ☐

Thing 3 ☐

DAY 3

Date

Thing 1

Thing 2

Thing 3

DAY 4

Date

Thing 1

Thing 2

Thing 3

DAY 5

Date

Thing 1

Thing 2

Thing 3

DAY 6

Date

Thing 1

Thing 2

Thing 3

DAY 7

Date

Thing 1 ______ ☐

______

Thing 2 ______ ☐

______

Thing 3 ______ ☐

______

Week 39 – REWARD

______

______

______

______

My mission in life is not merely to survive, but to thrive; and to do so with some passion, some compassion, some humor, and some style.

— Maya Angelou

WEEK 40

DAY 1

Date

Thing 1 ☐

Thing 2 ☐

Thing 3 ☐

DAY 2

Date

Thing 1 ☐

Thing 2 ☐

Thing 3 ☐

DAY 3

Date

Thing 1

Thing 2

Thing 3

DAY 4

Date

Thing 1

Thing 2

Thing 3

DAY 5

Date

Thing 1 ☐

Thing 2 ☐

Thing 3 ☐

DAY 6

Date

Thing 1 ☐

Thing 2 ☐

Thing 3 ☐

DAY 7

Date

Thing 1 ☐

Thing 2 ☐

Thing 3 ☐

Week 40 – REWARD

Stop and take your time to notice things and make those things you notice matter.

— Cecelia Ahern

WEEK 41

DAY 1

Date

Thing 1 ☐

Thing 2 ☐

Thing 3 ☐

DAY 2

Date

Thing 1 ☐

Thing 2 ☐

Thing 3 ☐

DAY 3

Date

Thing 1

Thing 2

Thing 3

DAY 4

Date

Thing 1

Thing 2

Thing 3

DAY 5

Date

Thing 1 ☐

Thing 2 ☐

Thing 3 ☐

DAY 6

Date

Thing 1 ☐

Thing 2 ☐

Thing 3 ☐

DAY 7

Date

Thing 1

Thing 2

Thing 3

Week 41 – REWARD

Discovering what you really want saves you endless confusion and wasted energy.

— Stuart Wilde

WEEK 42

DAY 1

Date

Thing 1 ☐

Thing 2 ☐

Thing 3 ☐

DAY 2

Date

Thing 1 ☐

Thing 2 ☐

Thing 3 ☐

DAY 3

Date

Thing 1

Thing 2

Thing 3

DAY 4

Date

Thing 1

Thing 2

Thing 3

DAY 5

Date

Thing 1

Thing 2

Thing 3

DAY 6

Date

Thing 1

Thing 2

Thing 3

DAY 7

Date

Thing 1 ☐

Thing 2 ☐

Thing 3 ☐

Week 42 – REWARD

*You don't get results by focusing on results.
You get results by focusing on the actions
that produce results.*

— Mike Hawkins

WEEK 43

DAY 1

Date

Thing 1

Thing 2

Thing 3

DAY 2

Date

Thing 1

Thing 2

Thing 3

DAY 3

Date

Thing 1

Thing 2

Thing 3

DAY 4

Date

Thing 1

Thing 2

Thing 3

DAY 5

Date

Thing 1 ______________________ ☐

____

Thing 2 ______________________ ☐

____

Thing 3 ______________________ ☐

____

DAY 6

Date

Thing 1 ______________________ ☐

____

Thing 2 ______________________ ☐

____

Thing 3 ______________________ ☐

____

DAY 7

Date

Thing 1 ☐

Thing 2 ☐

Thing 3 ☐

Week 43 – REWARD

We are what we repeatedly do. Excellence, then, is not an act but a habit.

— Will Durant

WEEK 44

DAY 1

Date

Thing 1 ☐

Thing 2 ☐

Thing 3 ☐

DAY 2

Date

Thing 1 ☐

Thing 2 ☐

Thing 3 ☐

DAY 3

Date

Thing 1

Thing 2

Thing 3

DAY 4

Date

Thing 1

Thing 2

Thing 3

DAY 5

Date

Thing 1 ☐

Thing 2 ☐

Thing 3 ☐

DAY 6

Date

Thing 1 ☐

Thing 2 ☐

Thing 3 ☐

DAY 7

Date

Thing 1 ☐

Thing 2 ☐

Thing 3 ☐

Week 44 – REWARD

This one step – choosing a goal and sticking to it – changes everything.

— Scott Reed

WEEK 45

DAY 1

Date

Thing 1 ☐

Thing 2 ☐

Thing 3 ☐

DAY 2

Date

Thing 1 ☐

Thing 2 ☐

Thing 3 ☐

DAY 3

Date

Thing 1 ☐

Thing 2 ☐

Thing 3 ☐

DAY 4

Date

Thing 1 ☐

Thing 2 ☐

Thing 3 ☐

DAY 5

Date

Thing 1

Thing 2

Thing 3

DAY 6

Date

Thing 1

Thing 2

Thing 3

DAY 7

Date

Thing 1 ☐

Thing 2 ☐

Thing 3 ☐

Week 45 – REWARD

A goal properly set is halfway reached.

— Zig Ziglar

WEEK 46

DAY 1

Date

Thing 1 ☐

Thing 2 ☐

Thing 3 ☐

DAY 2

Date

Thing 1 ☐

Thing 2 ☐

Thing 3 ☐

DAY 3

Date

Thing 1

Thing 2

Thing 3

DAY 4

Date

Thing 1

Thing 2

Thing 3

DAY 5

Date

Thing 1 ☐

Thing 2 ☐

Thing 3 ☐

DAY 6

Date

Thing 1 ☐

Thing 2 ☐

Thing 3 ☐

DAY 7

Date

Thing 1 ☐

Thing 2 ☐

Thing 3 ☐

Week 46 – REWARD

Goals provide the energy source that powers our lives. One of the best ways we can get the most from the energy we have is to focus it. That is what goals can do for us; concentrate our energy.

— Denis Waitley

WEEK 47

DAY 1

Date

Thing 1 ☐

Thing 2 ☐

Thing 3 ☐

DAY 2

Date

Thing 1 ☐

Thing 2 ☐

Thing 3 ☐

DAY 3

Date

Thing 1 ☐

Thing 2 ☐

Thing 3 ☐

DAY 4

Date

Thing 1 ☐

Thing 2 ☐

Thing 3 ☐

DAY 5

Date

Thing 1 ☐

Thing 2 ☐

Thing 3 ☐

DAY 6

Date

Thing 1 ☐

Thing 2 ☐

Thing 3 ☐

DAY 7

Date

Thing 1 ☐

Thing 2 ☐

Thing 3 ☐

Week 47 – REWARD

Avoid fragmentation: Find your focus and seek simplicity. Purposeful living calls for elegant efficiency and economy of effort—expending the minimum time and energy necessary to achieve desired goals.

— Dan Millman

WEEK 48

DAY 1

Date

Thing 1 ______ ☐

Thing 2 ______ ☐

Thing 3 ______ ☐

DAY 2

Date

Thing 1 ______ ☐

Thing 2 ______ ☐

Thing 3 ______ ☐

DAY 3

Date

Thing 1 ☐

Thing 2 ☐

Thing 3 ☐

DAY 4

Date

Thing 1 ☐

Thing 2 ☐

Thing 3 ☐

DAY 5

Date

Thing 1 ☐

Thing 2 ☐

Thing 3 ☐

DAY 6

Date

Thing 1 ☐

Thing 2 ☐

Thing 3 ☐

DAY 7

Date

Thing 1 ☐

Thing 2 ☐

Thing 3 ☐

Week 48 – REWARD

For fast-acting relief, try slowing down.

— Lily Tomlin

WEEK 49

DAY 1

Date

Thing 1 ☐

Thing 2 ☐

Thing 3 ☐

DAY 2

Date

Thing 1 ☐

Thing 2 ☐

Thing 3 ☐

DAY 3

Date

Thing 1 ☐

Thing 2 ☐

Thing 3 ☐

DAY 4

Date

Thing 1 ☐

Thing 2 ☐

Thing 3 ☐

DAY 5

Date

Thing 1

Thing 2

Thing 3

DAY 6

Date

Thing 1

Thing 2

Thing 3

DAY 7

Date

Thing 1 ______ ☐

Thing 2 ______ ☐

Thing 3 ______ ☐

Week 49 – REWARD

The benefits of working smart are just as profound: better health, often more money, a great work/life balance, more energy, a better self-esteem, exceptional productivity, and satisfaction with work.

— Ron Alvesteffer

WEEK 50

DAY 1

Date

Thing 1 ☐

Thing 2 ☐

Thing 3 ☐

DAY 2

Date

Thing 1 ☐

Thing 2 ☐

Thing 3 ☐

DAY 3

Date

Thing 1

Thing 2

Thing 3

DAY 4

Date

Thing 1

Thing 2

Thing 3

DAY 5

Date

Thing 1

Thing 2

Thing 3

DAY 6

Date

Thing 1

Thing 2

Thing 3

DAY 7

Date

Thing 1 ☐

Thing 2 ☐

Thing 3 ☐

Week 50 – REWARD

You don't have to make yourself miserable to be successful. It's natural to look back and mythologize the long nights and manic moments of genius, but success isn't about working hard, it's about working smart.

— Andrew Wilkinson

WEEK 51

DAY 1

Date

Thing 1 ☐

Thing 2 ☐

Thing 3 ☐

DAY 2

Date

Thing 1 ☐

Thing 2 ☐

Thing 3 ☐

DAY 3

Date

Thing 1 ☐

Thing 2 ☐

Thing 3 ☐

DAY 4

Date

Thing 1 ☐

Thing 2 ☐

Thing 3 ☐

DAY 5

Date

Thing 1

Thing 2

Thing 3

DAY 6

Date

Thing 1

Thing 2

Thing 3

DAY 7

Date

Thing 1 ☐

Thing 2 ☐

Thing 3 ☐

Week 51 - REWARD

I spend most of my time thinking about how to connect the world and serve our community better, but a lot of that time isn't in our office or meeting with people or doing what you'd call real work. I take a lot of time just to read and think about things by myself.

— Mark Zuckerberg

WEEK 52

DAY 1

Date

Thing 1 ☐

Thing 2 ☐

Thing 3 ☐

DAY 2

Date

Thing 1 ☐

Thing 2 ☐

Thing 3 ☐

DAY 3

Date

Thing 1 ☐

Thing 2 ☐

Thing 3 ☐

DAY 4

Date

Thing 1 ☐

Thing 2 ☐

Thing 3 ☐

DAY 5

Date

Thing 1 ☐

Thing 2 ☐

Thing 3 ☐

DAY 6

Date

Thing 1 ☐

Thing 2 ☐

Thing 3 ☐

DAY 7

Date

Thing 1 ☐

Thing 2 ☐

Thing 3 ☐

Week 52 – REWARD

That's been one of my mantras – focus and simplicity. Simple can be harder than complex: You have to work hard to get your thinking clean to make it simple. But it's worth it in the end because once you get there, you can move mountains.

— Steve Jobs

One part at a time,
one day at a time,
we can accomplish
any goal we set
for ourselves.

— Karen Casey

Congratulations!

You have completed 1092 goals for the year.

Take just a few minutes to reflect on your success and reward yourself for this accomplishment.

Look back over this journal to see everything you've done and consider how applying the "3 things a day" strategy has impacted your productivity, mental health, and attitude.

I hope you have found this journal useful and will consider this strategy as your permanent method for achieving your goals.

If you decide to purchase another 3 Things A Day journal to continue this habit, please contact us at support@barriedavenport.com for a discounted price.

Here's to your continued success!

Notes

Notes

Notes

Notes

Notes

Notes

Notes

Notes

Notes

Notes